Elementary Level
Workbook for Children
Ages 7-9 Years.

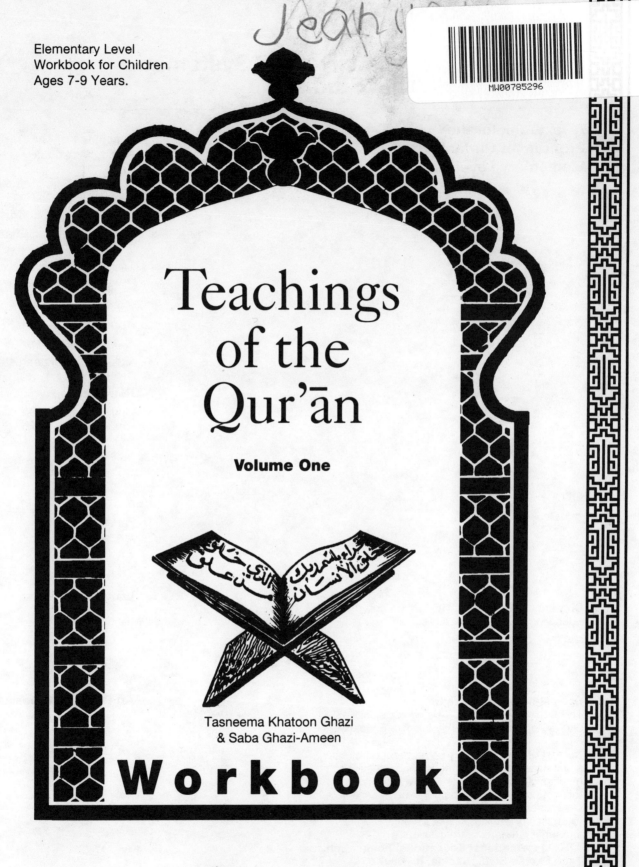

Teachings of the Qur'ān

Volume One

Tasneema Khatoon Ghazi
& Saba Ghazi-Ameen

Workbook

IQRA'
International Educational Foundation

Chicago

Part of a Comprehensive and Systematic Program of Islamic Studies

A Textbook for the
Program of Qur'anic Studies
Elementary Level

Teachings of the Qur'an,
Part 1, Workbook

Chief Program Editors:

Abidullah al-Ansari Ghazi
Ph.D. History of Religion, Harvard

Tasneema Khatoon Ghazi
Ph.D. Curriculum and Reading,
University of Minnesota

Approved by:

Rabita al-Alam al-Islami

Makkah Al-Mukarramah

Reviewers:

Ghulam Haider Aasi
Ph.D. History of Islamic Religion,
Temple University

Assad N. Busool
Ph.D. Arabic and Islamic Studies

Irfan Ahmad Khan
Ph.D. Philosophy, University of Illinois

Fadel Abdallah
(M.A. Islamic Studies,
University of Minnesota)

Language Editors:

Dr. Khwaja Moinul Hassan
(Ph.D. English Literature,
Purdue University)

Noura Durkee
M.A. Fine Arts, Stanford University

Art Direction & Design:

Jennifer Mazzoni
(B.A. Illustration,
Columbia College Chicago)

Library of Congress Control Card Number 95-76090
ISBN # 1-56316-111-7

TO PARENTS AND TEACHERS
(Read before you teach this textbook.)

We are pleased to introduce to this study guide for the textbook Teachings of the Qur'ān, Volume I. Study guides are an integral part of IQRA's Comprehensive Program of Islamic Education, along with their accompanying textbooks.

This workbook is written with the purpose of providing meaningful and interesting reinforcement to the children after they have finished reading a chapter in the textbook. Exercises are developed with the intentions of helping the students in grasping the main ideas, memorizing the basic facts, and comprehending the issues presented in the text. Furthermore, through these exercises an attempt has been made to enhance students' abilities in problem solving, sequencing, drawing inferences, evaluating, analyzing and synthesizing.

Each exercise corresponds to a lesson in the textbook. In order to benefit from the exercises, the teacher should read through the corresponding lesson in the textbook with the class and then ask the students to work on the exercise in the workbook.

The exercises provided in the workbook are developed with an understanding of the abilities and interests of 7 to 9 year olds.

It will be helpful to follow these strategies while teaching in the class:

◆ **Introducing the Lesson:** Read each lesson in the textbook with the children in the class.
◆ **Introducing the Vocabulary:** Discuss the meaning of each new word encountered in the lesson.
◆ **Reading and Reflection:** Ask the children to read the lesson again silently to themselves and to think about the specific issues dealt with in the lesson.
◆ **Asking Comprehension Questions:** After the children have read the lesson, ask questions (literal, inferential and critical) about the contents of the chapter.
◆ **Providing Practice:** Open the same lesson in the workbook and discuss the relevant exercise with the class. Help the students with the first problem, then ask them to work on the remaining exercises themselves.
◆ **Providing Feedback:** Always remember to look at the completed exercise and comment on the work. It is necessary for motivation. Rewarding good work encourages the children to do quality work.

Please keep in touch and send us your comments and/or suggestions:
IQRA' International Educational Foundation
7450 Skokie Blvd.
Skokie, IL 60077

IQRA's Note

بِسْمِ اللهِ الرَّحْمٰنِ الرَّحِيْمِ

Table of Contents

Teachings of the Qur'an: An Introduction

A. The baby fish were busy playing and got lost! Help them find their Mommas! **Match each question on the left with the correct answer on the right by coloring each baby and it's momma the same color!**

The first Surah of the Qur'an is ...

The Qur'an is divided into thirty ...

The language of the Qur'an is...

The angel that brought the Qur'an is...

Ajza

Arabic

Jibril

Al-Fatiha

B. For each of the statements below, **color the correct answer green.**

The language of the Qur'an is the _____ of the Arabic language.

good

better

best

The teachings of the Qur'an are meant for _____.

some people

all people

most people

The Qur'an is the _____ book of Allah (SWT).

last

first

second

The message of the Qur'an is (only) for _____.

Arabs of Rasul's time

people of our time

everyone for all times

A wahi is _____.

a revelation from Allah

a chapter of the Qur'an

sayings of the Prophet (s)

C. All Aboard! The train has got to get to Morroco but some of the wheels need to be changed. Daud, the engineer, needs you to help him put the correct wheels onto each compartment. **Color the train compartment and its matching wheel the same color.**

The first ____ of the Qur'an is called Alif Laam Mim

The Qur'an is Allah's ____ to Prophet Muhammad (s)

Juz

Surah

Ajza

Each chapter of the Qur'an is called a ____.

The plural of juz is _____.

The way the Prophet (s) talked, acted and lived is his ____.

Sunnah

Wahi

D. Every day you learn something new. Take a moment and think about some of the new things you learned today.

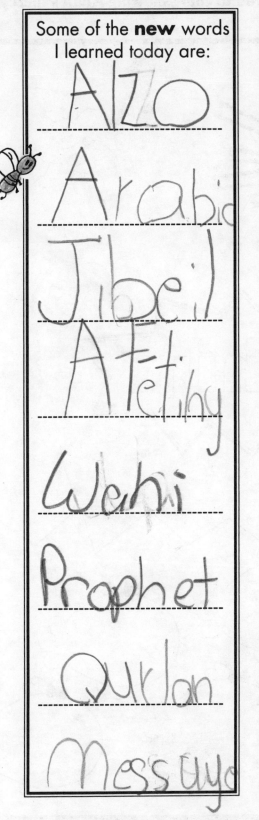

Some of the **new** words I learned today are:

Alzo

Arabic

Jibeil

A-feting

Wahi

Prophet

Qur'an

Messuya

Here is a drawing of something **new** I saw today:

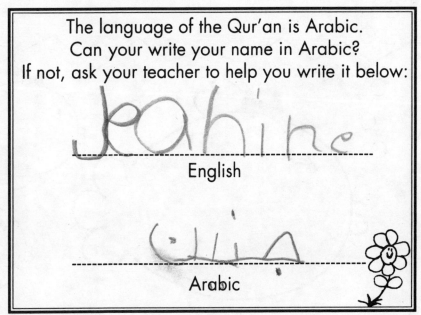

The language of the Qur'an is Arabic.
Can your write your name in Arabic?
If not, ask your teacher to help you write it below:

Jeahine

English

الجيا

Arabic

In The Name of Allah

A. Allah (SWT) is merciful. **Below is a pictures for you to color showing Allah's mercy.**

Ar-Rahim

B. In the space below, give an example of Allah's compassion to one of the following prophets

1. Prophet Nuh (A)
2. Prophet Ibrahim (A)

(If you need help, read <u>The</u> <u>Prophet</u> <u>of</u> <u>Allah,</u> volumes <u>I</u> and <u>II</u>)

_____

_____

_____

_____

_____

_____

C. Write the answers to the following questions in the space provided

1. How many names does Allah (SWT) have ? _____

2. Write any two of Allah's names: _____ , _____

3. We call Allah (SWT) All-Hearing because: _____

4. What is the name of the only surah in the Qur'an that does

   not begin with Bismillah _____

D. It's puzzle time!
Draw a line from each word on the left to its opposite meaning on the right.

 Merciful

 Reject

 Loving

 Cruel

 Accept

 Tawhid

 Angry

 Hateful

 Shirk

Happy

E. Color in the verse that should be recited before beginning any activity.
Fill in the two empty circles with any other activities.

Read

A. **Color the correct answer red. Color the rest of the picture any way you like.**

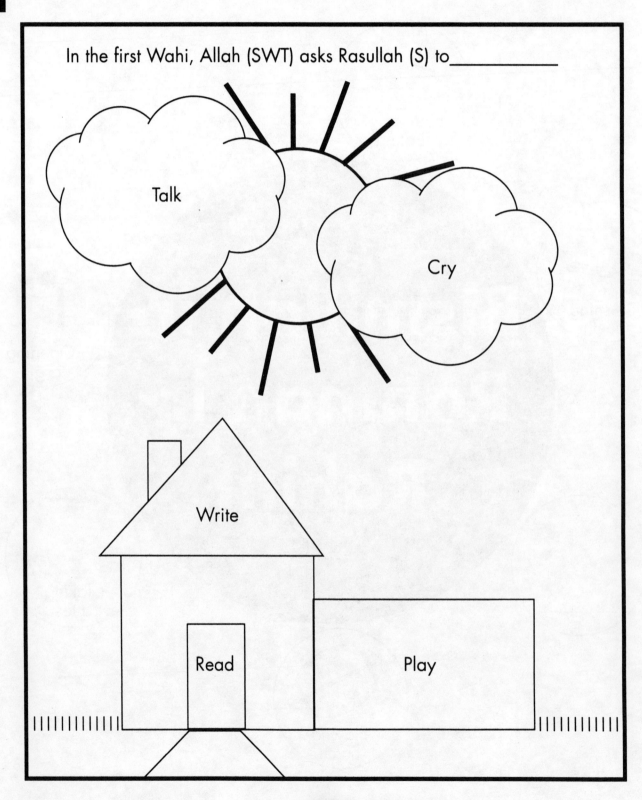

In the first Wahi, Allah (SWT) asks Rasullah (S) to_____

Talk

Cry

Write

Read

Play

B. The words of Allah (SWT) are in the **Qur'an.** The sayings of the Prophet (S) are called **Hadith.** In the picture below, color the shape with words from the Qur'an yellow and color the shape with Hadith purple.

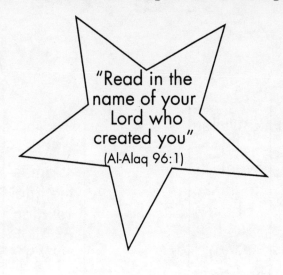

"Read in the name of your Lord who created you" (Al-Alaq 96:1)

"The best among you are those who learn the Qur'an and teach it to others"

C. **Number the 7 sentences below in the correct order**. The first one has been done for you. (see the last two paragraphs of page 5 of your textbook for help)

____ Angel Jibril (A) **again** ordered Rasulullah (S) to "Read!"

____ Rasulullah (S) replied "I cannot read"

____ Rasulullah (S) was in the Cave of Hira when Angel Jibril (A) came to him

__1__ Angel Jibril (A) asked Rasulullah (S) to "Read!"

____ Angel Jibril (A) hugged Rasulullah (S) tightly and asked him to "Read!"

____ Rasulullah (S) **again** replied "I cannot read"

____ Angel Jibril (A) then recited and Rasulullah (S) repeated after him.

D. The flags have flown off of their poles and you need to put them back!
Match the *cause* on the top with its *effect* on the bottom by coloring them the same co

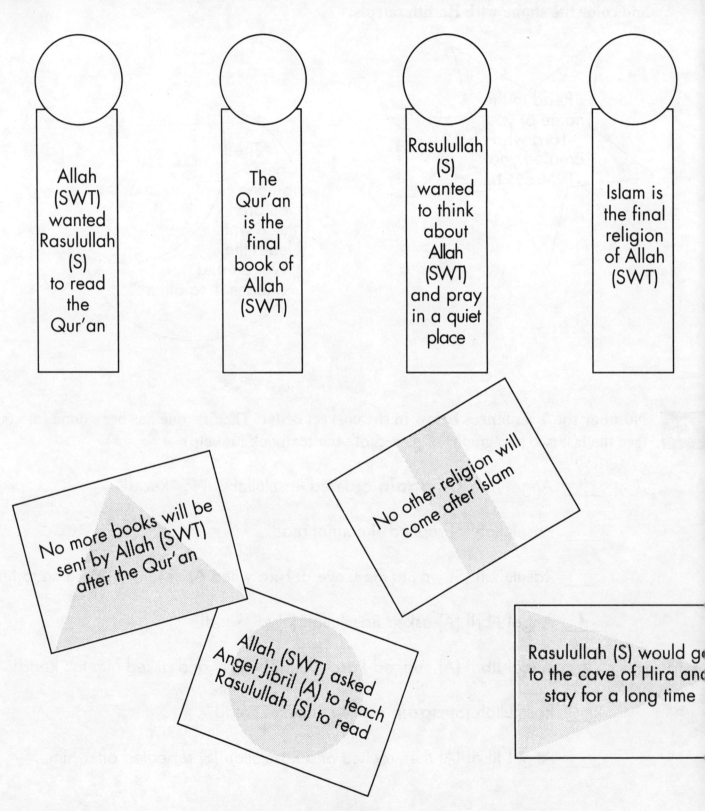

Allah (SWT) wanted Rasulullah (S) to read the Qur'an

The Qur'an is the final book of Allah (SWT)

Rasulullah (S) wanted to think about Allah (SWT) and pray in a quiet place

Islam is the final religion of Allah (SWT)

No more books will be sent by Allah (SWT) after the Qur'an

No other religion will come after Islam

Allah (SWT) asked Angel Jibril (A) to teach Rasulullah (S) to read

Rasulullah (S) would g[o] to the cave of Hira and stay for a long time

E. An adjective is a word used to describe a noun such as: pretty, tall, or wonderful.
Draw a line from the noun in each door, to the key which best describes it.

Allah (SWT)

Surah Al-Kawthar

Abu Jahl

1 generous
2 large
3 unkind

1 short surah
2 long surah
3 first surah

1 Muslim
2 caring
3 Mushrik

The Religion of Islam

A. Islam means a religion of peace. Close your eyes and **write five words that come to your mind as you think of the word peace.**

B. There were many Prophets of Allah. The clues below describe some of the Prophets of Allah. **Fill in the names and then color the sections of the butterfly**

The first Prophet of Allah was **A**_____ (A)   (color the **A**'s red)

The Prophet that turned a rod to a snake was **M**_____ (A)   (color the **M**'s yellow)

The Prophet that built an Arc was **N**_____(A)   (color the **N**'s purple)

The Prophet that could speak at birth was **I**_____ (A)   (color the **I**'s blue)

The Prophet that could speak to animals was **S**_____ (A)   (color the **S**'s green)

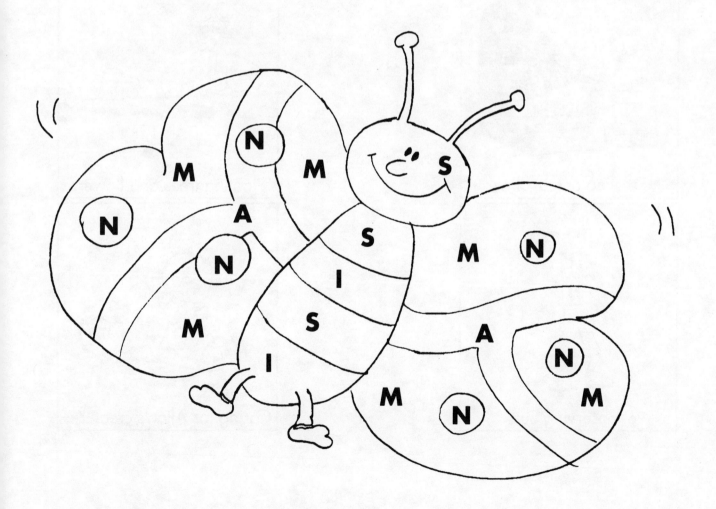

C. **Put a red "X" through all the activities that we should not do as Muslims**

Stealing from others

Hurting animals

Greeting one another

Planting trees and flowers

Not observing Sutr

Caring for Allah's creatures

D. **Match words on the left to their meanings on the right.**

TRUE	The life after death
SALIMA	Community
ISLAM	Whole
COMPLETE	Real, Right
AKHIRA	To be at peace
UMMAH	Religion of peace

The Qur'an: No Doubts

A. Below are some books from the school library.
Read the titles and **color the five Books revealed by Allah (SWT) in different shades.**

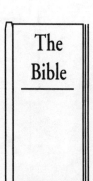

B. Allah (SWT) has given us the power to change some things, but there are many other things created by Allah (SWT) that **we** can not change.
Only Allah (SWT) has the power to make these things happen.
"I Can Change" or "I Can not Change" after each of the following phrase.

1. Hadith of Rasullah (S) _____

2. The Clothes you wear _____

3. The words of the Qur'an _____

4. The timing of the Salah _____

5. The books you read _____

6. The month of Ramadan _____

7. The time of sunrise _____

8. The Day of Qiyamah _____

9. The time you read the Qur'an _____

10. The direction of Qiblah _____

C. Help this young Muttaqi get to the Masjid by **tracing the correct path of good deeds in green. Remember: you can only move in the direction of the arrows.**

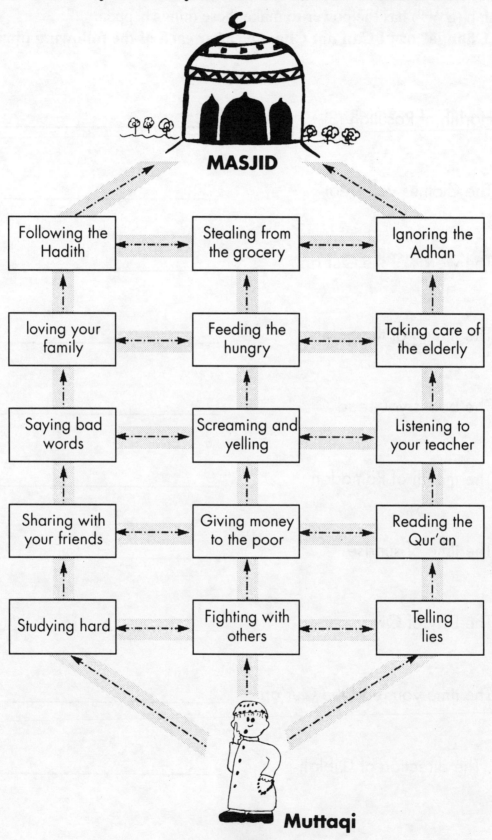

D. The Qur'an tells us that we should encourage good behavior and forbid what is wrong
For each of the following activities, circle "right" or "wrong"

1. Starting every job with bismillah   RIGHT   WRONG

2. Cheating on tests   RIGHT   WRONG

3. Showing respect to parents   RIGHT   WRONG

4. Offering five daily prayers   RIGHT   WRONG

5. Helping neighbors and friends   RIGHT   WRONG

6. Wasting water and energy   RIGHT   WRONG

7. Fasting during Ramadan   RIGHT   WRONG

8. Making fun of others   RIGHT   WRONG

9. Fulfilling your promises   RIGHT   WRONG

10. Using bad language   RIGHT   WRONG

The Qur'an: Easy to Remember

A. A miracle is **created** only by Allah (SWT). No human being, Angel, or Jinn can create a miracle, they can only **perform** the miracle with Allah's help.
Write the names of the Prophets that performed the miracles below with the help of Allah (SW

Prophet _____ (A)
could speak to animals

Prophet _____ (A) made
the camel come out of the mountain

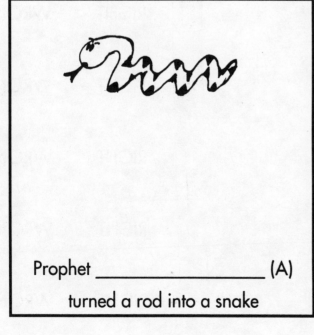

Prophet _____ (A)
turned a rod into a snake

The Qur'an was revealed to
Prophet _____ (S)

B. **For each of the statements below, circle the correct answer.**

1. The Qur'an is a Book of Allah (SWT) as is the _____.

   Tawrat

   Curious George

   I Love Madinah

2. The Qur'an is written in the Arabic language just as the ____
   is written in Hebrew.

   Sahih Bukhari

   Tawrat

   Caps for Sale

3. The Qur'an was revealed to Prophet Muhammad (S) just as the Injil was
   revealed to Prophet _____.

   Musa (A)

   Nuh (A)

   Isa (A)

4. The Qur'an is the last book of Allah (SWT) just as Prophet _____
   is the last Prophet of Allah (SWT)

   Adam (A)

   Muhammad (S)

   Nuh (A)

C. For each of the following statements, circle "Right" or "Wrong".

1. You can memorize the entire Qur'an in Arabic even if you do not know the Arabic language — RIGHT — WRONG

2. A Hafiz is a person who has memorized the entire Qur'an — RIGHT — WRONG

3. Huffaz are a group of people who do not know the Qur'an — RIGHT — WRONG

4. Muslims should try to understand the Qur'an — RIGHT — WRONG

5. A Hafiz can create a miracle — RIGHT — WRONG

6. The Qur'an is written in a beautiful style and its message is pure — RIGHT — WRONG

7. The Qur'an is too difficult for anyone to understand — RIGHT — WRONG

D. Help each bee find its place on the flower.
Draw a line from each bee to the word in the petal that is opposite in meaning.

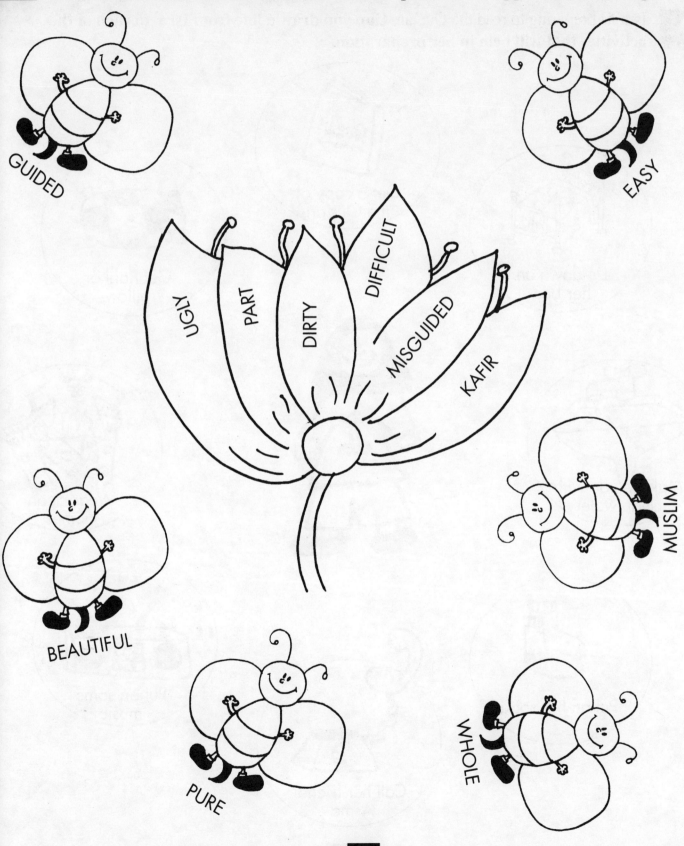

Read The Qur'an

A. Isra' is preparing to read the Qur'an. **Can you draw a line from Isra' to each of the activities that will help in her preparation.**

Lie down on her bed

Get a copy of the Qur'an

Get Rahl or pillow

Make Wudu with clean water

Wear clean clothes

Put on her socks

Call her friend Asma

Put on some music

B. Read and color in the squares below.

This is the Qur'an

It was revealed in the Arabic language

The meaning is written in English

The Qur'an is the message of Allah

It has 30 parts

I read it everyday

I try to understand and learn the Qur'an

Sometimes I read it out loud

and sometimes I read it quietly

C. WHO? WHAT? WHY?

For each of the sentences below write which words tell: WHO, or WHAT, or WHERE.

<u>EXAMPLE:</u>

The Qur'an guides us to the right <u>path</u> of Islam.

WHAT guides us to the right path of Islam? _*the Qur'an*_

WHO?

1. Allah (SWT) warns us against the wrong path of Shirk

   WHO warns us against the wrong path of Shirk? _____

2. We must learn to read the Qur'an.

   WHO must learn to read the Qur'an? _____

3. Muslims all over the world recite the Qur'an in Arabic.

   WHO recites the Qur'an in Arabic? _____

WHAT?

1. The Qur'an is sent for all people in this world.

   WHAT is sent for all people in the world? _____

2. A person who memorizes the Qur'an by heart is a hafiz.

   WHAT does a hafiz memorize? _____

3. Barakah is a blessing which comes from Allah (SWT)

   WHAT is Barakah? _____

WHERE?

1. The first verses of the Qur'an were revealed in the Cave of Hira.

   WHERE were the first verses of the Qur'an revealed? _____

2. Muslims go to Mecca to perform Hajj.

   WHERE do Muslims go to perform Hajj?_____

3. Muslims face the Ka'bah in Mecca when they pray.

   WHERE do Muslims face when they pray? _____

D. Find the words that are opposite in meaning.
Draw a line from each word on the left to its opposite on the right

KUFR

BARAKAH

DAY

SUCCESS

FAILURE

NIGHT

IMAN

PUNISHMENT

How to Read the Qur'an

A. The rungs on the ladder have all fallen off except the ones on the top and bottom!
Can you draw a line from the rungs on the right to the ladder on the left,
in the order that the events took place? Number 1 and 7 have been filled in to help you

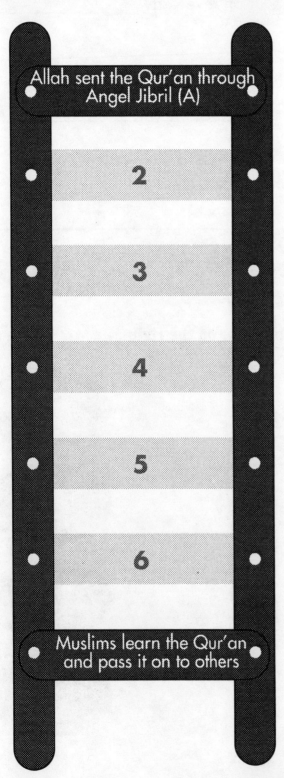

Allah sent the Qur'an through Angel Jibril (A)

2

3

4

5

6

Muslims learn the Qur'an and pass it on to others

Rasulullah (S) memorized the words of the Qur'an

The Sahabah memorized it

Rasul (S) recited the Qur'an to his Sahabah

Angel Jibril (A) recited the Qur'an to Muhammad (S)

The Sahabah recited the Qur'an to other Muslims

B. **For each of the questions below, circle the correct answer.**

1. Who taught Prophet Muhammad (S) how to read?

Prophet Adam (A)

The Sahabah

Angel Jibril (A)

2. To whom did the Prophet (S) teach the Qur'an?

Angel Jibril (A)

Prophet Musa (A)

Sahabah

3. To whom will YOU teach the Qur'an Insha allah?

Prophet Muhammad (S)

Your friends and children

The Sahabah

4. Why do we recite the Qur'an in Arabic?

Because Arabic is a different language

Because the Qur'an was revealed in Arabic

Because the Arabs speak Arabic

C. The drivers below have lost their way. Can you put each car in the correct garage? **Match the word in the car to the correct definition in each garage.**

A person who has memorized the Qur'an

A person that knows Tajwid & Tartil

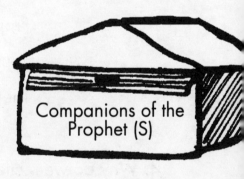

Companions of the Prophet (S)

The art of reciting the Qur'an

D. For each of the VERBS below, find the correct noun.

VERB	NOUN
READ	
PRAY	
LEAD	
KUFR	
RECITE	

Choose nouns from this list:

KAFIR   READER   RECITATION

LEADER   PRAYER

Iman

A. Can you uncover the secret letter?
Color the words in each <u>row</u> that do not belong blue. Color the rest of the words green.

1 ALLAH	ONE	MESSEN-GER	MERCILESS	KAFIR	KIND
2 PROPHETS	ADAM (A)	NUH (A)	JIBRIL (A)	SALIH (A)	MUSA (A)
3 PRAYERS	MAGHRIB	ASR	RAMADAN	FAJR	ISHA
4 HOLY BOOKS	TAWRAT	SUHUF	HADITH	QUR'AN	ZABUR
5 ANGELS	JIBRIL (A)	SALIH (A)	NUH (A)	FATIMA (R)	MIKA'IL (A)

B. Iman is belief. We believe in some things even though we can not see or touch them. Each of the peas in the peapod below has a word. **Color the words that we can not see or hear but still believe in green. Color the rest of the words yellow.**

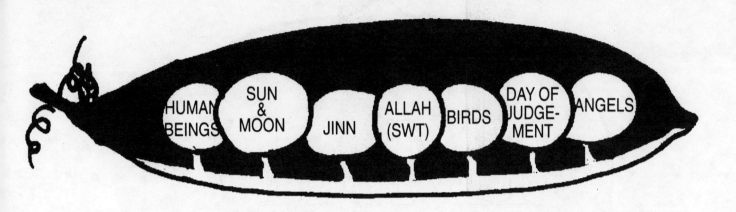

HUMAN BEINGS   SUN & MOON   JINN   ALLAH (SWT)   BIRDS   DAY OF JUDGE-MENT   ANGELS

C. **In the box below, circle the names of the Prophets that have received Books from Allah (SWT)**

Prophet Adam (A)   Prophet Ibrahim (A)

Prophet Nuh (A)

Prophet Daud (A)   Prophet Muhammad (S)

Prophet Salih (A)   Prophet Ismail (A)

Prophet Musa (A)

Prophet Isa (A)

D. **Color in the picture below with the five pillars of Islam.**

E. Write the answers in the blocks (there are some clues),
then write the letters in the gray boxes at the bottom of the page to reveal a secret word!

The last book revealed by Allah (SWT)

| ▓ | U | | |

Fasting is one of the five____ of Islam

| | ▓ | | L | | | |

Shahadah is the _____ that there
is no god but Allah and Muhammad
(S) is the messenger of Allah

| ▓ | | | | F |

We perform _____ five times a day.

| S | | ▓ | |

The pilgrimage every Muslim makes
once in their lifetime is called the...

| | ▓ | J | |

The _____ is to share one's savings
with the poor and needy.

| | | K | | ▓ |

| ▓ | ▓ | ▓ | ▓ | ▓ | ▓ |

Blessings of Allah

A. On the right is a picture showing many of Allah's blessings.
No one can really count them **all**, but count as many as you can and **write them below**.
[Remember, there are many Blessings that you can not see, such as friendship and the wind]

---   ---

---   ---

---   ---

---   ---

---   ---

---   ---

B. Allah (SWT) has blessed us with parents, teachers and friends.
In the house below, draw some of the people you love.

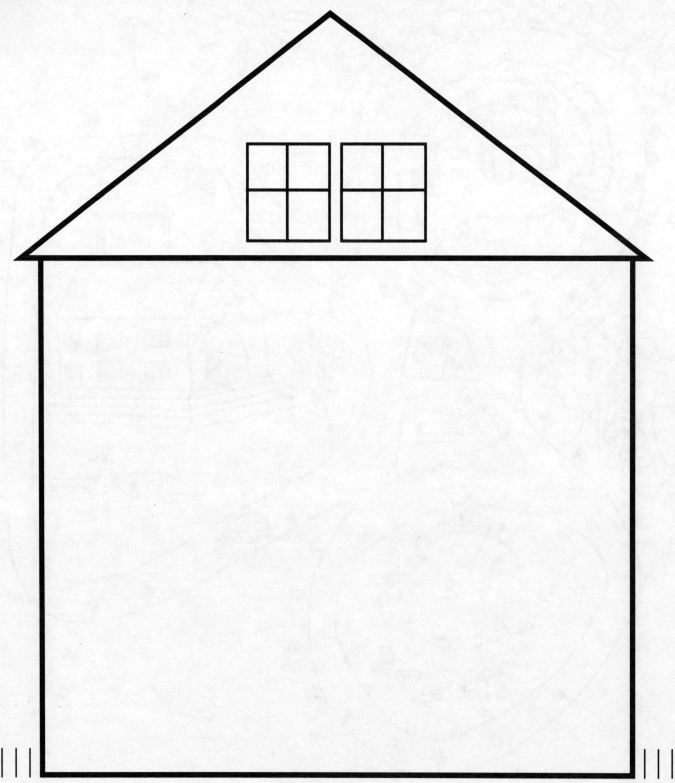

C. In each of the groups below, one of the words does not rhyme with the others
Read each group of words and circle the word which does not rhyme.

Example:

	Share	Fare	Care	(Power)

1. Eat   Heat   Mat   Meat

2. Good   God   Wood   Hood

3. Bad   Sad   Fat   Mad

4. Brain   Train   Grain   Blame

5. Snow   Row   Blow   Blot

6. Made   Paod   Grade   Stay

The Will of Allah (SWT)

A. This is Ahmed:  **Help him say the right things in the following situations.**

Ahmed wants to travel to Makkah for Hajj.

 **Ahmed should say:** " _____ "

Ahmed worked hard in school and today is his graduati

 **Ahmed should say:** " _____ "

Ahmed woke up early in the morning and enjoyed a beautiful sunrise.

Ahmed should say:

"

-- "

Ahmed's teachers like his work and his Islamic manners very much.

Ahmed's Mom says:

"

-- "

Ahmed's class has lost their hamster.

They should say:

"

-- "

B. Can you plant the seeds in the right pot?
For each of the statements in the seeds below, draw a line to the planter that contains the correct words that should be said.

INSHA-ALLAH

AL-HAMDU LILLAH

SUBHAN-ALLAH

MASHA-ALLAH

"This boardgame is just what I wanted!"

"The mountains are beautiful"

"I will travel to London one day"

"You have grown so much"

C. In the treetops below are three of the beautiful names of Allah (SWT).
Write the meanings of the names in the trunks and color them.

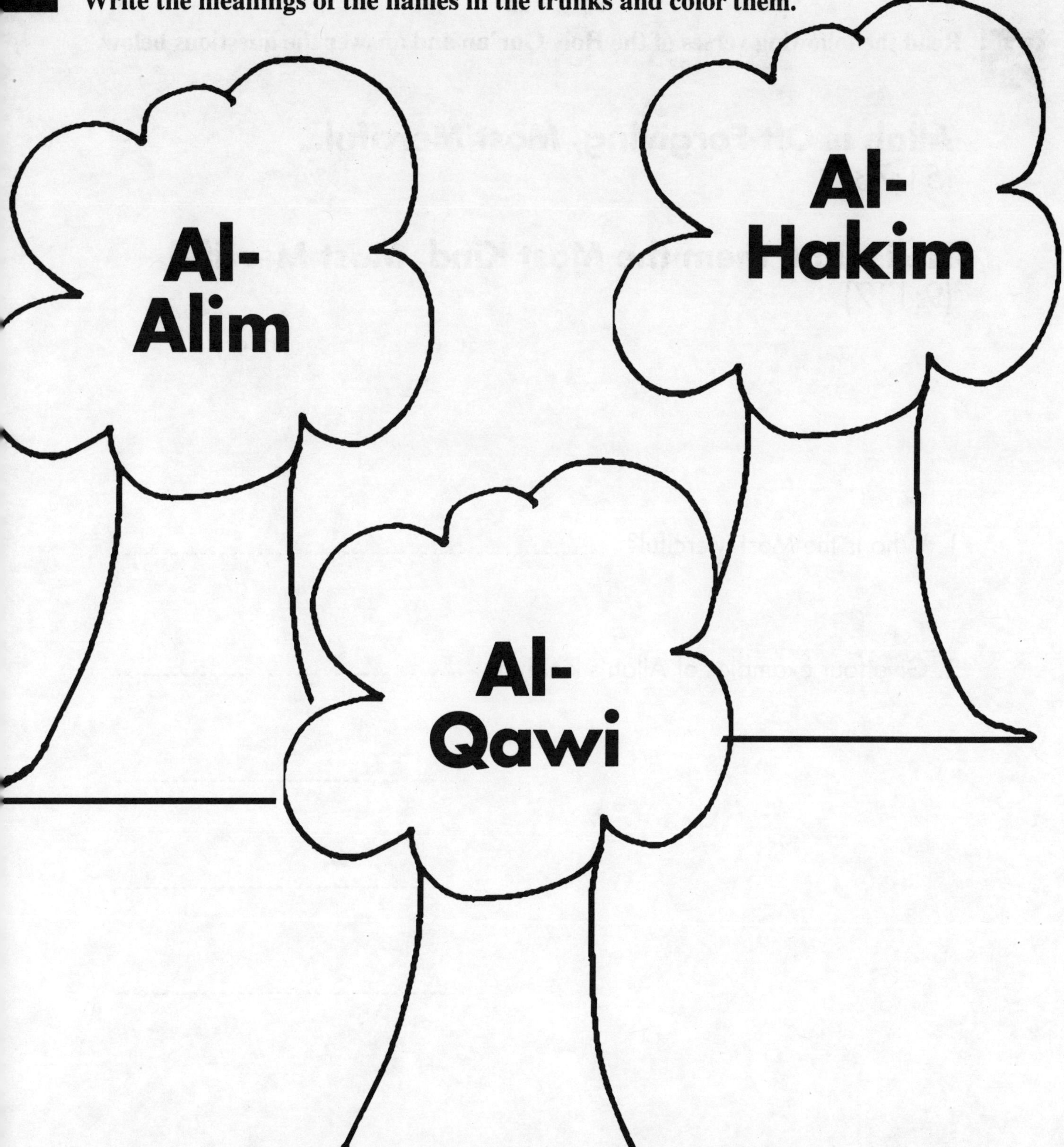

Al-Alim

Al-Hakim

Al-Qawi

The Help of Allah (SWT)

A. Read the following verses of the Holy Qur'an and answer the questions below.

Allah is Oft-Forgiving, Most Merciful.
(51:73)

He is unto them the Most Kind, Most Merciful.
(9:117)

1. Who is the Most Merciful? --

2. Give four examples of Allah's kindness: -----------------------------------

----

B. There are many ways to thank Allah (SWT) for His kindness.
Color the pictures below and in the empty box, draw a picture of a way in which you would like to thank Allah (SWT) for His Blessings.

Sharing with others

Keeping the Masjid clean

Visiting the sick

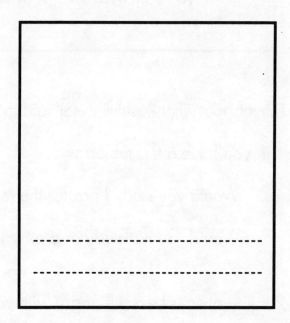

C. Read and think about the following story then answer the questions below.

> **One day, Prophet Muhammad (S) was sitting under a tree when a bedouin came and asked him,**
>
> "Oh Rasulallah (S), should I tie my camel to the tree before I sit down to rest or should I leave him untied and trust in Allah (SWT) to care for him?"
>
> **Rasulullah (S) answered,**
>
> "Tie your camel to the tree and trust in Allah (SWT) that He will protect him.

Think about what Rasulullah (S) said to the Bedouin and **decide what you would**

1.If you have a test tomorrow

Would you study hard for the test and pray to Allah (SWT) that you do well?
or
Would you not study and pray to Allah (SWT) that you do well?

2.If you always become angry with your friends and get into fights with them,

Would you try very hard to control your anger and pray to Allah to help you
or
Would you pray to Allah for help and not try to control your anger.

D. Below are three shapes. **Find the word that belongs in each shape.**

In the **triangle**, write the word that means to lose
In the **circle** , write the word that means strong belief.
In the **square,** write the word that means to allow something to be done.

WORDS: PERMISSION, DEFEAT, TRUST

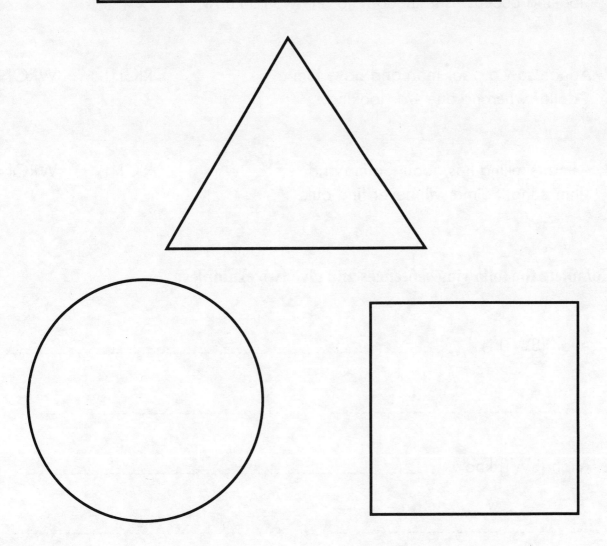

Allah is (SWT) Near

A. For each of the following statements, circle "Right" or "Wrong".

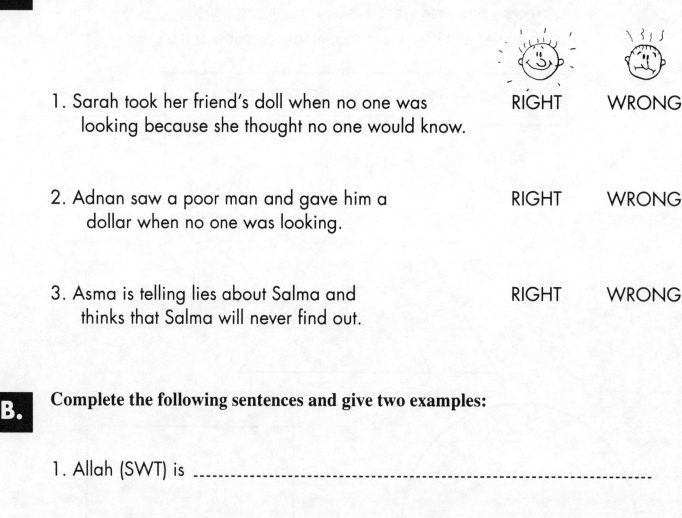

1. Sarah took her friend's doll when no one was looking because she thought no one would know.

RIGHT   WRONG

2. Adnan saw a poor man and gave him a dollar when no one was looking.

RIGHT   WRONG

3. Asma is telling lies about Salma and thinks that Salma will never find out.

RIGHT   WRONG

B. Complete the following sentences and give two examples:

1. Allah (SWT) is --

    -------------------------------------- , --------------------------------------

2. Allah (SWT) knows --

    -------------------------------------- , --------------------------------------

3. Allah (SWT) loves --

    -------------------------------------- , --------------------------------------

C. **Match the words in the cups with their meanings in the saucers.**

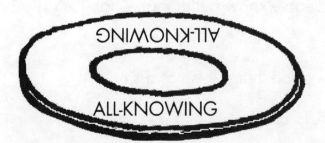

Shirk: The Greatest Sin

A. For each of the following statements, **circle "True" or "False"**.

1. Muslims believe that there is no god but Allah (SWT) TRUE FALSE

2. All Muslims believe that Allah (SWT) is one,
 and that no one has power besides him. TRUE FALSE

3. Allah (SWT) likes the Mushrikun. TRUE FALSE

4. People that believe that there are other
 gods besides Allah (SWT) are Mushrikun. TRUE FALSE

5. A Mushrik believes that jinn or the sun
 have the same power that Allah (SWT) does. TRUE FALSE

6. We should pray to Allah (SWT) to save us from Shirk. TRUE FALSE

7. Some people know better than Allah (SWT) TRUE FALSE

8. Shirk is good thing. It is not a sin. TRUE FALSE

B. A partner is someone that you can do things equally with.
In the spaces below **write down what type of partners each picture shows.**

Sarah and Yasmin
play together
and share their toys.

They are:

F _____

Arif and Salma have
two children and love
each other very much

They are:

M _____

Musa and Rashid work
together and they own a
computer company.

What kind of partners
are they?

B _____

C. Read the Ayah below, then answer the questions.

Whoever accepts partners with Allah, he has indeed invented a great sin."
(An-Nisa 4:48)

1. What do you call someone
   who accepts partners with Allah (SWT)? _____

2. What does Allah say
   in the Qur'an about such a person? _____

Kufr: The Worst Sin

A. For each of the following statements, **circle the correct relationship**.

1. **Iman** is to a Muslim
   as **Kufr** is to a ...   MUSHRIK   KAFIR   MUSLIM

2. **Tawhid** is to a Muslim
   as **Shirk** is to a ...   KAFIR   JEW   MUSHRIK

3. **Qur'an** is to a Muslim
   as **Tawrat** is to a ...   HINDU   JEW   CHRISTIAN

B. There are many non believers in the world today. They may be kind, generous, and well educated, but they do not believe in Allah (SWT).
For each of the sentences below, put a "N" next to the things that the non believers believe and a "M" next to the things that Muslims believe.

	N OR M?
1. People developed from apes a long time ago.	
2. Everyone is created by Allah (SWT) and Adam (A) and Hawwa (R) were the first parents.	
3. We will be judged on the Last Day.	
4. There is no right or wrong. We can do whatever we like.	
5. Allah (SWT) is merciful to everyone.	

C. **Guide each rocket to its planet or star by matching the correct meanings to the words.**
Use different colors and different types of lines (. . . . ., ____, - - - -, >>>>>, etc.)

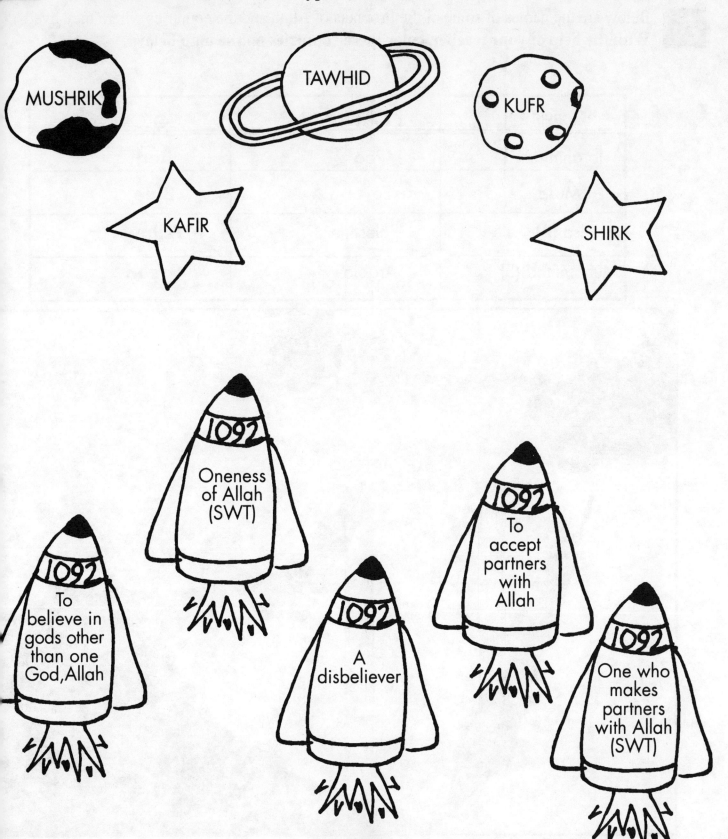

Messengers of Allah (SWT)

A. Below are the names of some of the Prophets of Allah and the countries where they lived. **With the help of your teacher, color these countries on the map below.**

PROPHET	COUNTRY	COLOR
Ibrahim (A)	Iraq	**Red**
Musa	Egypt	**Blue**
Isa (A)	Palestine	**Yellow**
Muhammad (S)	Arabia	**Green**

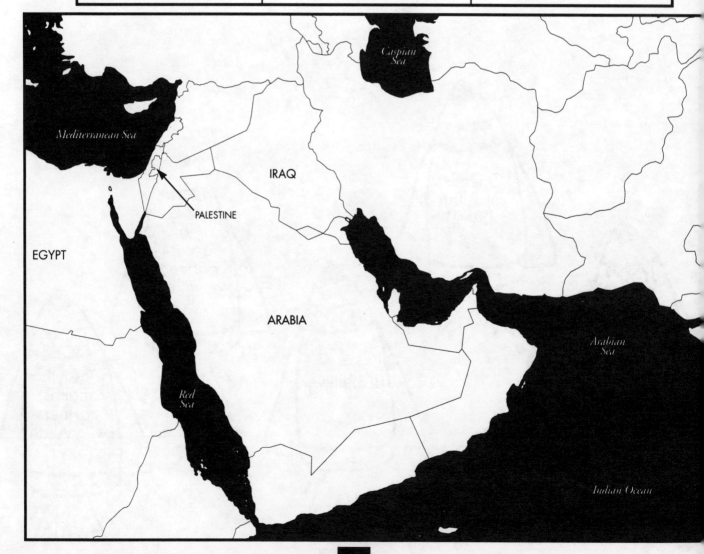

B. Read the bold statements below.
If the numbered statement best describes the President of a country put a "P" next to them and if it best describe s a Messenger of Allah put a "M" next to it.

**A messenger of Allah is a very special teacher and leader.
He brings Allah's message to all the people. He is guided by Allah.**

**A President of a country is chosen by the people of that country.
He is the leader of only the people in his country.**

	P OR M?
1. This person's message is the Wahi (direct words) of Allah (SWT)	
2. This person is a leader for only one country.	
3. Abraham Lincoln was one of these types of people.	
4. This person teaches people about life and Akhirah.	
5. This person's message is for all people in the world.	
6. This person is chosen by the people of a country.	
7. Some of these people received books from Allah (SWT).	
8. Musa (A) was one of these types of people.	
9. This person is a leader for a limited number of years (4 - 8 years)	

C. Think about the messengers of Allah (SWT). What kind of people were they?
Color the words below that you think describe them best.

STUCK UP
SMART
BRAVE
SELFISH
FOOLISH
LOVING
STRONG
KIND
TIMID

D. In the blocks below write the names of as many Messengers of Allah as you can between Prophet Adam (A) and Prophet Muhammad (S).

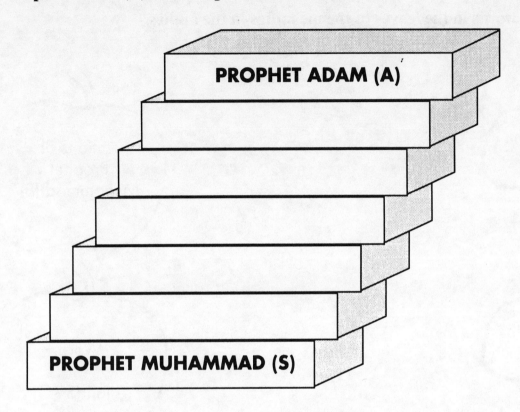

PROPHET ADAM (A)

PROPHET MUHAMMAD (S)

E. Draw a line from the words on the right to the words on the left that have the same meaning.

REVEAL   ONENESS

COVER UP   HIDE

MESSENGER   GIVE IN

SURRENDER   SHOW

TAWHID   NABI

The Best Model to Follow

A. Match the words in the leaves to the meanings in the apples.

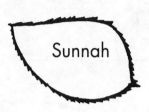

Sunnah

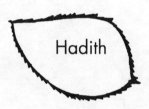

Hadith

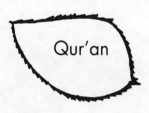

Qur'an

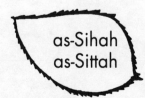

as-Sihah
as-Sittah

Actions of
Prophet
Muhammad (S)

Word
of
Allah (SWT)

The six
books of famous
Hadith

Sayings of
Prophet
Muhammad (S)

B. Everything that Prophet Muhammad (S) said and did is an example of Allah's message to us. **For each of the statements below, decide which actions you would do and cross out the actions that you would not do as a follower of Prophet Muhammad(S).**

Arif promised he would clean his room but went out to play instead

Saad recycles his soda cans when he is finished

Zahra returned Rima's dress after borrowing it

Karim brought his mother a glass of water to drink

Saira is helping a blind man cross the street.

Tahira is feeding the birds.

Kulsum is cheating on her homework

Yunus is beating his younger brother

Ahmed hears the Adhan and prays right away.

C. In the grid below, color the activities that Prophet Muhammad (S) did in his life green and the activities he did not do in his life blue to reveal a special pattern!

AN IMAM	A KING	A MECHANIC	A FATHER
A PRESIDENT	A HUSBAND	A TEACHER	AN UNKIND PERSON
A LIAR	A MESSENGER OF ALLAH	A FRIEND	A BUILDER
A LISTENER	AN EMPEROR	AN AIRPLANE PILOT	A KIND PERSON

D. Help Uncle Khalid get to the library so that he can read about the Sunnah and Hadith of Prophet Muhammad (S).

The Example of Rasulullah (S)

A. This lesson tells us a number of things that Allah (SWT) did for Rasulullah (S). **In the circles below, list three of them.**

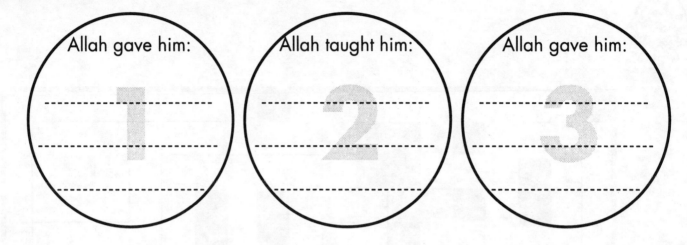

Allah gave him:

1

Allah taught him:

2

Allah gave him:

3

B. This lesson also tells us a number of things that Rasulullah (S) showed and taught us.. **In the rectangles below, list three of them.**

He showed us how to	He taught us how to	He taught us how to
----------------	----------------	----------------
----------------	----------------	----------------
----------------	----------------	----------------
----------------	----------------	----------------
----------------	----------------	----------------
----------------	----------------	----------------

C. Allah sent Rasulullah (S) as an example for us.
For each of the statements below, select the adjective that describes Rasulullah best.

1. People used to call Rasulullah (S) Al-Amin, the _____ .

TRUSTWORTHY   RELIABLE   THE MOST TRUSTWORTHY

2. Rasulullah (S) brought the _____ message of Allah (SWT) to us.

FIRST   FINAL   THIRD

3. Rasulullah (S) suffered many hardships but he was always patient and calm.
He was the _____ person.

CALM   CALMER   CALMEST

D. Decide whether the word pairs below are Synonyms (Similar in meaning)
or Antonyms (opposite in meaning). **Put a check in the "=" box if they are synonyms
and a check in the "<>" box if they are antonyms.**

WORD PAIRS	=	<>
LOVE/HATE		
FRIEND / ANSAR		
GUIDE / MISGUIDE		
FINAL / LAST		
JANNAH / JAHANNAM		
EXAMPLE / MODEL		

Love of Rasulullah (S)

A. Read lesson 19 in your book. In the first paragraph there are pairs of words that describe Rasulullah (S). **Complete the pairs below**.

1. Kind and _____.

2. Caring and _____.

3. Wise and _____.

B. Rasulullah (S) and Ummahat ul-Mu'minin are the best examples for us to follow. **For each of the situations below, write what you would do as a Muslim.**

1. You hear your father calling the adhan but your favorite TV show is on.

    I would -- .

2. After dinner, your mother is too tired to do the dishes but your friend is over.

    I would -- .

3. Your friend throws a candy wrapper on the sidewalk when the garbage can is o
the corner

    I would -- .

C.

Suppose Rasulullah (S) was living in this world today and he was coming to visit you. **What would you like to do with him? What would you like to show him? Fill in the lists below.**

I would invite these
people to meet him:

I would help my
parents cook:

At home,
I would show him:

I would take him to
these places:

The Books

A. Allah has sent books with his wahi to some of the prophets.
For each of the books below, **color the star purple if the book was sent by Allah (SWT) and color the star yellow if the book was written by a person.**

SUHUF

GOOD NIGHT MOON

RAMONA THE PEST

JAMAL'S PRAYER RUG

QUR'AN

INJIL

MY BOOK OF DU'A

PSALMS

B. For each of the books below, read the description and try to find out the name of the book. **Write the name in the space provided.**

It is the last book of Allah (SWT).
It was sent to a prophet who lost his parents at a young age.
Allah (SWT) has promised to protect this book

Allah gave this book to the prophet who had the most beautiful voice.
It was sent after the Tawrat and before the Injil.
Its name begins with the last letter of the alphabet.

This book was revealed to a prophet who could talk when he was a baby.
It was sent before the last book of Allah.
People have changed many of Allah's words in this book

It was revealed to a great prophet on Mount Sinai.
Its name begins with the letter "T".
It was sent for the children of Israel.

It was the first book of Allah (SWT).
It was sent to the prophet who was the father of Prophet Ismail.
It is lost now.

D. **For each of the statements below, circle the correct answer.**

1. We call a Prophet who received a book from Allah (SWT) a/an:

NABI

RASUL

ANGEL

ANSAR

2. All the books of Allah (SWT) teach us about:

OUR DUTIES TO ALLAH (SWT)

THAT ALLAH (SWT) HAS PARTNERS

NOT PAYING ZAKAH

ALL OF THE ABOVE

3. The final book of Allah is:

THE QUR'AN

THE TAWRAT

THE GOSPEL

THE ZABUR

4. Allah's laws ask people to

OBSERVE SAWM

PERFORM HAJJ

OFFER SALAH

ALL OF THE ABOVE

E. Can you solve the puzzle?
Use the clues at the bottom to fill in the missing letters and complete the arch!

```
¹A □ □ □ ⁶L
□         □
□         □
□         □
²Z □ □ □ □   ³S □ □ □ ⁷F
□              □
□              □
□              □
⁴R □ □ □ L   ⁵I □ □ □ L
```

ACROSS
1. Some of the prophets received Allah's book through ____ Jibril.
2. Allah's law that begins with the letter "Z"
3. Prophet Ibrahim received this book.
4. Prophets who received books are called_ ___.
5. In Arabic, the Gospel is called the _____.

DOWN
1. Tawhid is the oneness of _____.
2. Prophet Dawud received this book.
6. A Muslim, L_____ Rasul (S) and Ummahat ul-Mu'minin
7. The Qur'an is the F____ book of Allah (SWT)

The Mala'ikah: the Angels

A. Allah (SWT) has given the angels very special qualities.
Color the lightbulbs below yellow if they contain a quality of the Mala'ikah.

Made of
Nur

Can not
see us

Always
busy

Disobey
Allah
(SWT)

We
can
see them

Take
different
forms

Partners
of
Allah
(SWT)

In charge
of
Jannah

Servants
of
Allah

B. In each of the boxes below, write the name of the Angel that the box describes.

ANGEL

Comes to people at the time of death

ANGEL

Makes sure that we get enough rain

ANGEL

Will blow a trumpet on Judgement Day

ANGEL

Brought Allah's wahi to the prophets

C. Match the words on the left to the meanings on the right.

SUR   PEACE BE TO YOU ALL

JANNAH   TRUMPET

AS SALAMU 'ALAI-KUM   HELL

JAHANNAM   HEAVEN

Al-Akhirah

A. Match the words in the "-" sign to their opposites in the "+" signs by connecting them with a line.

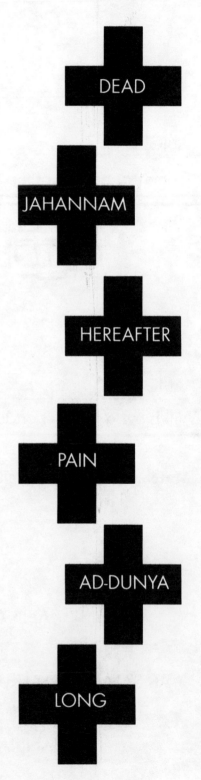

JANNAH

SHORT

AL-AKHIRAH

BORN

AD-DUNYA

PLEASURE

DEAD

JAHANNAM

HEREAFTER

PAIN

AD-DUNYA

LONG

B. Those who do good works will be rewarded with Jannah.
Color the flowers below that contain the beliefs of a Muslim.

PROPHETS OF ALLAH

NO LIFE AFTER DEATH

AKHIRAH

WORSHIP IDOLS

ANGELS OF ALLAH

QUR'AN THE BOOK OF ALLAH

Five Arkan: The Five Pillars

A. For each of the illustrations below, **write the name of the pillar that is illustrated.**

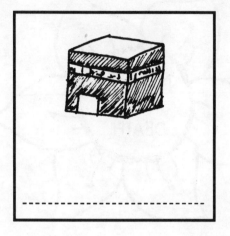

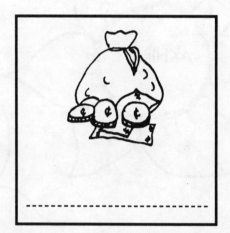

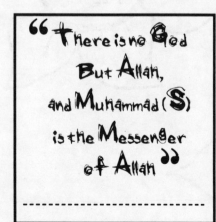

"There is no God
But Allah,
and Muhammad (S)
is the Messenger
of Allah"

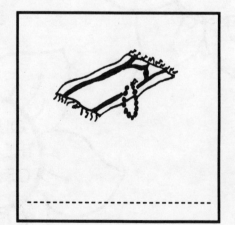

B. Read the bold statement below then answer the questions.

Being born in a Muslim family does not make one a Muslim. Neither does having a Muslim name.
A Muslim is one who believes in the teachings of the Qur'an and acts on those teachings.

1. Farhana's dad teaches Qur'an at an Islamic School.

   Both Farhana and her father

   act on the teachings of the Qur'an.

   Is Farhana a Muslim?   YES   NO

2. Adam goes to church on Sunday

   He does not follow the teachings of the Qur'an

   Is Adam a Muslim?   YES   NO

3. Jill has many Muslim friends.

   She does not believe in Allah (SWT)

   and that Muhammad (S) is His last mesenger.

   Is Jill a Muslim?   YES   NO

4. Ahmed's parents are Muslim.

   Ahmed fasts in Ramadan and reads the Qur'an

   Is Ahmed a Muslim?   YES   NO

C. The Qur'an contains the words of Allah (SWT).
The Hadith are the sayings of the Prophet (S).
Color the circles with Hadith Blue and the circles with Ayaat from the Qur'an Purple.

Allah told us, "So know that there is no God except Allah.' (47:19)

Prophet Muhammad (S) has said " Whosoever visits Kabah, the house of Allah and does not bad deeds or evil actions he returns as pure as the new born baby" (Muslim)

Allah has said, "Indeed Salah safeguards from shameful and evil acts" (29:45)

Allah says "When the Qur'an is read, listen to it with attention and do not talk" (7:204)

Allah has told us " Whoever obeys the Messenger, indeed obeys Allah" (4:80)

Prophet (S) said, "The best among you are those who learn the Qur'an and teach it to others" (Bukhari)

D. Fard or Obligatory means something Allah (SWT) has asked us to do
and we must do **all** the time.
**Draw a line from the letters that contain acts whch are FARD to the mailbox.
Cross out the others.**

Shahadah: Allah

A.   Color the names of Allah (SWT) below and learn them by heart.

B. Find the words that go together. **For each of the numbers below write the correct word in the space provided.**

ALLAH (SWT) HAS NO:

1. SONS or _____   [MOTHERS, DAUGHTERS]

2. BOYS or _____   [SISTERS, GIRLS]

3. AUNTS or _____   [MEN, UNCLES]

4. FATHER or _____   [MOTHER, AUNT]

5. BROTHER or _____   [BOY, SISTER]

C. Match the words on the left to the meanings on the right.

KUFR	TO BELIEVE THAT ALLAH HAS PARTNERS
SHIRK	TO SHARE POWER
GLORIFIED	PRAISED
PARTNER	NOT BELIEVING IN ALLAH

Shahadah: The Messenger

A. Recite the Shahadah with your teacher and freiends in the class.
Color the Shahadah in the space below.

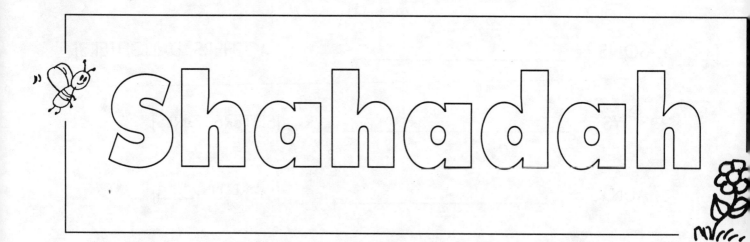

B. Two parts of the Shahdah have been separated in the mountains below.
Find them and bring them together by coloring them both green.

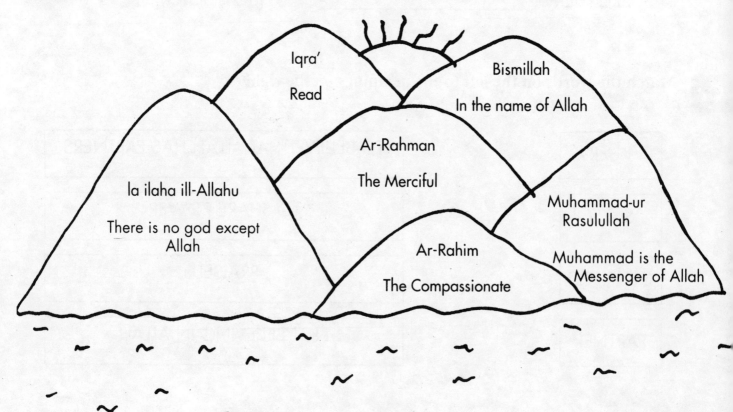

C. Nabi-ullah is a word made out of two words: NABI and ALLAH. It means Allah's nabi.
Combine each of the words below with "Allah" to make a compound word.

Allah's Rasul

Rasul _____

Allah's beloved

Habib _____

Allah's Words

Kalam _____

Allah's Servant

Abd _____

Allah's Message

Wahi_____

D. In the coconut tree below, color the leaves which describe Prophet Muhammad (S) gree
Color the rest of the leaves yellow. Color the trunk and coconuts brown.

Recieved the Qur'an

Used to drive a car

Watched television

A human being

Lived in the U.S.A

Last Nabi of Allah (SWT)

Was a servant of Allah (SWT)

E. In the Qur'an, Allah (SWT) says,

**Indeed Allah and the angels sent salutation on the prophet.
O' Believers, send Salutation and your Salam upon him.
[Al-Azhab 33:56]**

In thecaterpillar below, write what we must say when we hear the name of our
Prophet Muhammad (S) then color the caterpillar all diferent colors.

Enjoin Salah

A. Color the pictures about *salah* below.
Draw lines from each word to the matching picture.

PILLAR

ADHAN

JAMA'AH

MASJID

IMAM

B. For each of the word pairs below, circle the word that comes first.

ADHAN   or   IQAMAH

FAJR PRAYER   or   ASR PRAYER

WU'DU   or   SALAH

C. For each of the sentences below, circle the correct answer.

1. Salah is the _____ pillar of Islam.

    First

    Second

    Last

2. It is Fard to pray _____ times a day.

    Two

    Three

    Five

3. We should try to offer Salah _____ .

    Alone

    With Jama'ah

C.   In the frame below, **draw a picture of the masjid where you pray.**

D. Match each word to its correct meaning by **coloring the paint brush and its bucket the same color.**

ADHAN   IQAMAH   FARD   JAMA-AH

First call for prayer   Group behind the Imam   What we have to do   Second call to prayer

The Sawm: The Fasting

A. Study the Islamic calendar below and **fill in the blanks to complete the sentences**.

Islamic Calendar

MUHARRAM	**SAFAR**	**RABI'-AL-AWWAL**
RABI'-AT-THANI	**JAMADA AL-AWWAL**	**JAMADA AT-THANI**
RAJAB	**SHA'BAN**	**RAMADAN**
SHAWWAL	**DHUL QI'DAH**	**DHUL HIJJAH**

1. Ramadan is the _____th month of the Islamic Calendar.

2. The month of _____ comes before Ramadan.

3. The month of _____ comes after Ramadan.

B. In each of the boxes below, write your favorite things to eat and drink for *Iftar*.

My favorite fruit is:

My favorite drink is:

My favorite vegetable is:

My favorite food is:

C. Match the words on the left to the meanings on the right.

IBADAH   FASTING

SAWM   MONTH IN WHICH WE FAST

RAMADAN   WORSHIP

FARD   OBLIGATION

The Zakah

A. In the hand below, two of the five pillars of Islam are shown.
Write the other three in the remaining fingers, then color the hand.

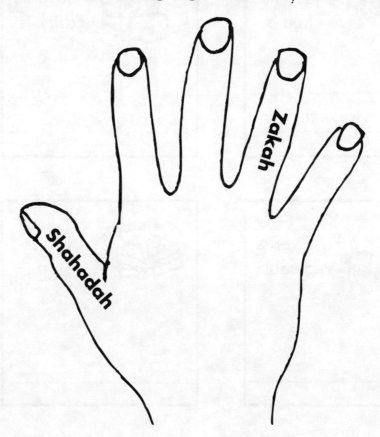

B. After reading lesson 28 in your textbook, check the ideas which were presented to you.

☐ 1. When we pay Zakah we please Allah (SWT).

☐ 2. We pay Zakah to the poor and needy by sharing our wealth with the

☐ 3. Children and poor adults should also pay Zakah

☐ 4. Zakah can be given to relatives.

C. For each of the statements below, circle **TRUE or FALSE**

1. Zakah is fard on a Muslim that has money and wealth.   TRUE   FALSE

2. Salah and Sawm are fard on every healthy adult Muslim.   TRUE   FALSE

3. Zakah is not a fixed amount of our savings.   TRUE   FALSE

4. Zakah should be paid to the rich.   TRUE   FALSE

D. Match the coins to the bills! **For each of the bills below, choose one of the three coins which is closest in meaning and color it yellow.**

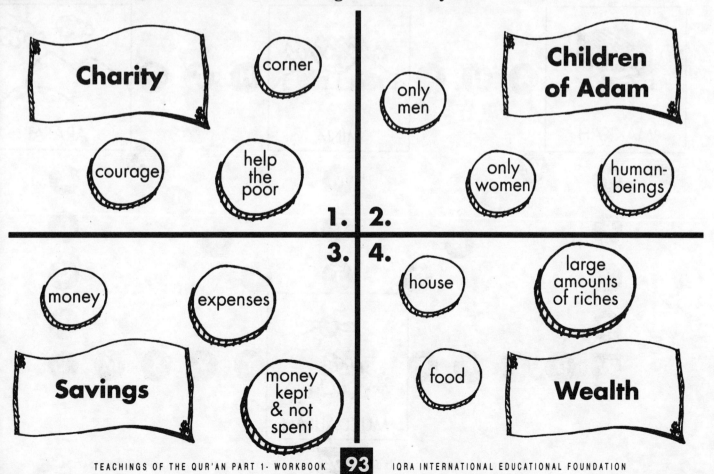

The Hajj: The Pilgrimage

A. Follow the correct path of Hajj starting from Jeddah by connecting the circles with the letters "H-A-J-J".

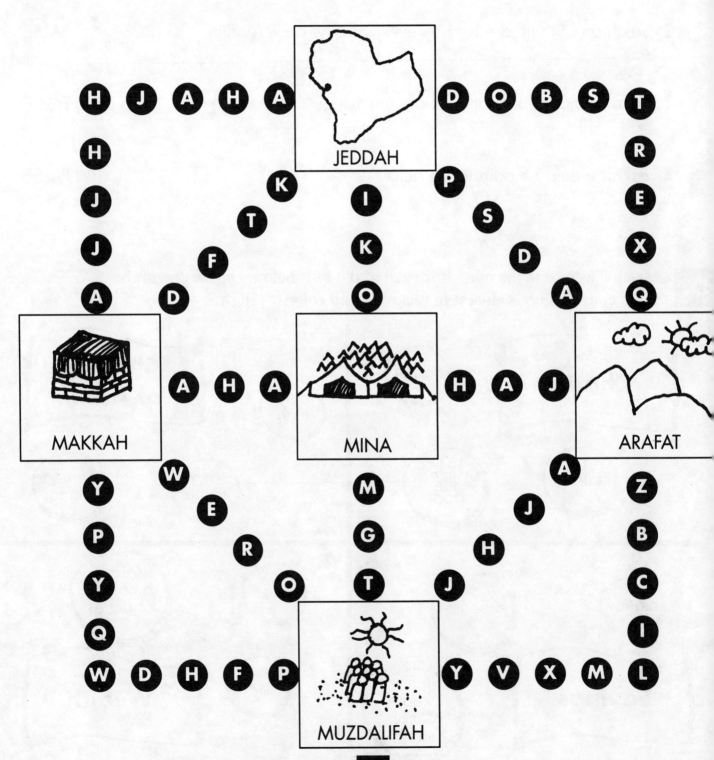

B. Draw a line from each picture to the word that describes it.

| BAIT-ULLAH | IHRAM | AL-HAJJAH | AL-HAJJ |

C. For each of the statements bellow, circle **TRUE or FALSE**

1. Hajj is fard on every person.   TRUE   FALSE

2. Muslims from different countries meet during Hajj.   TRUE   FALSE

3. All Muslims are the Ummah of Prophet Muhammad (S).   TRUE   FALSE

4. Children have to perform Hajj before they turn 12.   TRUE   FALSE

5. You can wear anything you want during Hajj.   TRUE   FALSE